A CHANCE ENCOUNTER?

(Author Unknown)

FOUR STAR BOOKS, Inc.
Historical Books Division
Publishers
Grants Pass, Oregon

128 S.W. I Street
Grants Pass, Oregon 97526-2813
503-955-2742
Fax: 503-955-2745

I T WAS DECEMBER 23ʳᵈ. This was an evening flight from New York to Los Angeles; we departed at six o'clock. Dinner had already been served and cleared away, empty glasses and coffee cups had been collected. The rush to the rest rooms was over, and most of the many passengers were tucked inside blankets, sleeping. I was alone in a row of five seats near the back of the plane. I was lucky; there were very few empty seats on this flight. Here and there a bright shaft of light from an overhead reading lamp pierced the cabin atmosphere and disappeared down into the seat below it.

I liked this scene on night flights. It always made me think of the line in *A Visit from St. Nicholas*: "And they all settled down for a long winter's nap." Although there's absolutely nothing reassuring about a jet aircraft flying at 36,000 feet, these night scenes always soothed me. There was no noise except the constant drone of the engines; no movement but the occasional rocking of the plane. I leaned back, not really trying to sleep, but feeling no need to stay awake either.

I was just drifting mentally when the stewardess startled me: "Excuse me, Mr. Fare," she whispered, leaning down, looking straight into my face. "We have a lady in First Class who's not feeling well and needs to lie down. Would you mind changing seats with her this evening?"

I responded without even having to think: "Sure."

I followed my "escort" up the aisle towards the curtained First Class section. Coming down the aisle on the other side of the plane was a steward helping an older woman along. That's the lady I'm changing seats with, I thought. But then how did they know I'd say yes? I then realized that I didn't have a choice in this matter at all . . . .

She held the First Class curtain aside for

me to enter. I thanked her, stepped through, and looked around. First class had its own galley, its own rest rooms, and everything was bigger and more spacious than it was back in coach. There were two empty seats and I wondered which one would be mine.

"Here you are," the stewardess smiled, motioning to the empty seat on the aisle in the front row, next to a man in the window seat.

"Thank you," I said, lowering myself into the large, wide, leather "lounger" and buckling the seat belt around me. It was so roomy here. I looked about, familiarizing myself with these new surroundings.

Questions began to march through my mind: How much does a First Class seat cost? Who are these people? How much money do they make? Obviously they know I came from the coach section and don't belong here . . . .

"May I offer you something to drink, or perhaps a snack, Mr. Fare?" It was the First Class stewardess, and was she gorgeous! Her beauty intimidated me, and I stammered: "Uh, yes, um, please. Yes, I'd like a mineral water."

I'm sure she noticed my nervousness, but her pleasant smile never changed. "Would you like carbonated or still water?" she asked patiently. I'd never been asked this before.

"Uh, carbonated, please," I was feeling glad this episode was over.

But it wasn't. "Would you care for a lemon or lime wedge with that?" she persisted. If her expression weren't so sweet, I'd claim she was mocking me with all these questions.

"Yes, um, lime, please," I answered, wondering what she could possibly ask next.

"Very good, and would you care for a bowl of mixed nuts or perhaps a plate of fruit and cheese?"

Oh, no, another decision! "No, thank you. Just the water will be fine, thanks." She smiled even more broadly, turned, and then disappeared into the galley a few steps away.

I was beginning to feel a little more comfortable in this new environment. The stewardess returned with my glass of water (a real glass, not plastic) and placed it and a coaster on a handy little tray she pulled from the front of the wide, table-sized armrest between my fellow passenger and me.

This new experience of being in First Class was too good to sleep through so I sat there, wide-eyed, sipping my drink, looking at everything, taking it all in. For all my observation, however, I had barely noticed the man next to me in the window seat.

"Excuse me, please," he was saying, already standing and waiting for me to move my feet for him to exit our row.

"Oh, sure. Excuse *me*." I hardly had to move at all really; there's plenty of space between rows in First Class. I began to wonder what he does . . . .

He returned, stopped at our row, and smiled slightly as if he were bothering me again. I know him! . . .

"Thank you very much," he said as he stepped past me and took his seat.

"Not at all," I replied, smiling at him, using this opportunity to get a good look at his face. It *was* him! I was sitting next to Frank Dean, probably the greatest life insurance salesman of all time. He's *the best*. He's a living *legend*!

The average person wouldn't know Frank Dean; he's an insurance industry icon. These days he handles only big cases, and works as a high-priced consultant. I first heard of him more than twenty years ago when my Dad entered the insurance industry. I was in junior high school then and remember my Dad coming from his Company's national convention, where Frank Dean was the keynote speaker. I don't recall very many specifics; I just mostly remember how excited my Dad was after hearing this man speak. For months — no, *years* — afterwards he would quote Mr. Dean or recite some small story the great man had told to illustrate one of his points.

Years later, struggling to support my wife and children, I tried my hand at selling life insurance and I don't think I ever respected my father more than then, when I discovered how challenging and frustrating a career it is.

Many, many times I thought of my Dad and Frank Dean during those long, hard times during my stint as an insurance salesman. I felt that I would never be in their league, however. Selling insurance wasn't something I enjoyed; I did it for only two reasons: To work for myself, and to try to make lots of money quickly. But the agency I worked for had all the ethics and integrity of a sandlot carnival. I yearned for a happier, more successful, and more decent place, the kind that I associated with people like my Dad and Frank Dean. You might say that I wanted to trade my sandlot carnival for a DISNEYLAND!

Next, I found myself in the real estate business, and achieved a modicum of success. I made a name for myself locally — in the Southern California area — and a real estate publisher approached me to put my knowledge on paper. I did, and my book was a top seller in his company's catalog. That's when he invited me to speak at one of the seminars he sponsored around the country. I started locally and soon found myself on more and more of these night flights, criss-crossing the United States. My encounter with Frank Dean followed a talk in Manhattan that morning. I was headed home, on what turned out to be an auspicious journey . . . .

"Mr. Dean? Is it you?" I instantly realized how stupid this sounded, but too late to take back the words. I sat there, eyes wide in anticipation, but also feeling very embarrassed and uncomfortably warm.

A smile crept across his face. He was looking down, and finished buckling his seat belt. Then he looked at me, stuck his hand out, and said, "Yes, I'm Frank Dean. How do you do?"

I must have looked like a small child who saw Santa Claus for the first time. I grabbed his hand and shook it way too long, but he didn't seem to mind. "How do you do, sir. I'm Bill Fare."

"Are you in insurance, Bill Fare?" he asked, smiling.

"Yes, well, uh, I used to be. And so was my Dad."

"Oh, so insurance runs in the family —," he smiled.

"Well, yes. My Dad was fairly successful at it. I tried awhile but just couldn't make a go of it."

He smiled, nodded, and then . . . silence! He was very pleasant and polite, but after all, I was the one who started this conversation. I made a quick mental evaluation of the situation and decided that if there was going to be a conversation here, I'd have to be the one to keep it going. The thought that this may be inconsiderate crossed my mind, but suddenly an enormous pressure built up in me; I felt as if I had a million questions to ask this giant.

The world's leading businesses and top executives were paying thousands of dollars to consult Frank Dean, and here I was sitting right next to him! I figured I'd better begin quickly, before he started reading, writing, or sleeping . . . .

"My Dad thought the world of you, Mr. Dean. He first heard you speak in New York, at Mutual Of New York's (the company he represented) national convention."

He looked over and smiled.

"I was just a kid then, but I still remember how much of an impression you made on him. I always knew you were a great man by the way my Dad would bring up your name over the years. He respected you very much. And so did I — err, I still do — just because of how highly he spoke of you."

"Thank you, Bill. And what do you do now?" By the way he asked this, I knew he was leading up to something more than small talk.

"Oh, I'm somewhat of a specialist in real estate and I speak for the publisher who discovered me," I smiled, making quote marks with my fingers when I said the word "discovered."

"Oh, an author! Is your book doing well?" he asked.

"Yes, moderately well, sir. It's not in bookstores or anything like that; it only appeals to people who are interested in real estate investments," I explained, making sure not to sound like I was bragging.

"It's funny where life takes us, isn't it? How do you explain your success?" he asked, looking me squarely in the eyes. This was no casual question. Mr. Dean was leading up to something . . . .

"Well, sir, from all the books I've read, and all of the seminars and classes I've attended, there are supposedly ways to visualize what we want and that vision will materialize. Whatever you can conceive and believe, you can achieve . . . ."

Mr. Dean laughed when I said this. I felt that warm flush again, embarrassed, as if I had said something really inane.

"I'm not laughing at you, Bill. I'm laughing at myself. I used to teach exactly what you just said. And worse, I used to believe it. Well, not really believe it, but I repeated it so often that I convinced myself it was true. Have you found any of it to be true, Bill?"

Now my mind was racing. "Well, well —, no. No, it's never worked for me, but . . . no! It never did." I suddenly realized that I couldn't explain my success, that it wasn't actually the result of dedication or belief, that it had just — well — "happened," or had it? Strangely, I felt a sense of relief saying this out loud to another human being. I had certainly thought it enough times, but I always dismissed this as doubt and suppressed it. But just now, here with Mr. Dean, as I said it aloud I knew I had spoken the truth. A great sensation of relief came over me. Mr. Dean evidently could see this too.

"Bill, you have just taken an extremely important step in your life. You have just done something very few people ever do, and I'm not exaggerating when I say this: You have reached a milestone. If you stay on this track, you'll make it all the way home." Mr. Dean nudged me on the arm and seemed genuinely delighted.

"What exactly do you mean, Mr. Dean?"

"Bill . . ." Mr. Dean had something important to tell me and was trying to find just the right way to say it. He tightened his lips, shifted his head slightly to the side, and looked past me for a moment. I was keenly alert, ready to grab every word he offered me. But the words weren't coming. He was still considering just the right way to put what he was about to tell me.

My mind began to wander now as I looked into his face and waited. He was a very pleasant and peaceful man. He had to be well into his 60s. He wasn't what I considered handsome, or even good looking, but he had a calmness and a strength about him that was inviting. I wanted to hear what this man had to say; somehow I knew that he didn't waste time on small talk.

" . . . Bill, isn't there something that always bothers you and tells you that everything's not alright?"

I hesitated for a moment. At first I wondered if he was accusing me of being a hypochondriac — suspecting that I thought something was wrong with me all the time. But then I realized he didn't mean aches and pains; he meant a general "dark-cloud" feeling that my whole world isn't right. How did he know?!

"Yes," I nodded, "that's exactly how I feel most of the time."

"Well that's how most people feel their entire lives. And that feeling is what runs their lives, all the way to the grave. Have you ever heard how Henry David Thoreau described it? Most men lead lives of quiet desperation and go to the grave with the song still in them."

I must have looked forlorn or dejected.

"Bill, this isn't bad news — it's *great* news! What if the entire world suffered from a plague, but everything everyone was trying to cure it with didn't work? And then someone came along who understood the plague and how to begin its cure — wouldn't that be great news?"

"Yes," I answered. But I noticed that I really didn't mean yes, and that puzzled me. It *would* be great news, so why couldn't I just come out and say that? Why didn't I actually believe this obviously correct statement? My eyes wandered off . . . .

"Bill, the very thing that has you wondering about your answer right now is the culprit. *It's* what's wrong — not the world!" He knew my response had been given with mixed feelings. He knew I had answered the question based on logic, but not from conviction.

"That puzzled look on your face, Bill, is evidence that you're at precisely the spot you need to be — one that very few people ever reach, by the way — to open yourself to a great secret that will be revealed to you. All illuminated men through the ages spoke and wrote of reaching this very place you're now at, Bill."

"They did?" That sounded so dumb, but it was all I knew to say.

"Yes they did. Robert Frost probably put it best of all when he wrote 'Two roads diverged in a wood, and I took the one less traveled by, and that has made all the difference.'

"And now it's your job to get to this place of puzzlement, of uncertainty, of *not* knowing as often as you can remember," he smiled.

Now my mind was beginning to reel. Why did these few, simple words Mr. Dean just say have such a powerful impact on me? For some reason, a vision of David and Goliath came to mind.

"Bill, we have very little time here together; this plane will land soon and we may never see each other again. A seed has been planted here tonight and with the proper nourishment it will grow beyond anything you can imagine (remember the Biblical mustard seed?). In fact, don't imagine anything at all because that will only limit you!" Mr. Dean's face and eyes were aglow now. He had sensed something — some potential in me — that he was fervently determined to cultivate. Deep down I knew he was entrusting me with some wonderful, powerful secret he knew. I also sensed that I had better keep quiet and not ask any of the multitude of questions that were scrambling to the front of my brain. I settled back in my seat, barely able to keep from shouting, Come on! Out with it!

"For as long as you've been alive, you've followed your thoughts, those same thoughts that have told you — falsely — that you need only to 'conceive and believe;' you've taken your directions from them. You've become so identified with them, so entangled and enmeshed in them, that you now believe you and your thoughts are one and the same. There is very little separation now between your thoughts and you; it's all pretty much running on automatic, at an unconscious level. About the only separation you're aware of is when you don't act on your violent thoughts, those thoughts you're ashamed of and would never reveal to anyone else."

How does he know about these? I wondered.

"The fact is, Bill, we don't create our own thoughts — we receive them. We're not thought-making machines, as we all suppose; rather, we're like radios that merely receive."

How does he know this? Where did he learn it?

"Don't be concerned with the why's and wherefore's of this now, Bill. Just listen and take it in as best you can. As you study and travel this path, all those questions clamoring in your brain now will be answered.

"Our minds are incredible computers really, and more and more, science proves this to be true. Your brain is a powerful problem-solving computer that was meant to provide practical solutions to practical problems: How to grow and provide food for yourself, how to earn a living, how to repair mechanical devices . . . . But at an early age, we allow this mind to become our master. The mind makes an excellent slave, but it's a horrible master.

"Did you get angry today, Bill?"

"Yes," I replied cautiously, remembering several times I had become angry that day.

"How about anxious?"

"Yes." In fact, I had been anxious most of this day.

"And depressed?"

"Yes, that too — occasionally." But my answer wasn't completely true, for I was depressed more than occasionally.

Mr. Dean shifted in his seat. I could tell he was considering how to make his next point as clear and concise as possible.

"Where has anger ever gotten you, Bill?" he asked calmly.

I thought for a moment and then answered

his question: "Nowhere."

"Actually, it's gotten you *less* than nowhere, hasn't it? Do you see that anger only hurts yourself and others? And many times you get angry toward someone else and he or she doesn't even know it! So then who does that anger hurt?"

"Just me," I reasoned.

"Not very intelligent, wouldn't you say?"

"That's right; it's actually very stupid," I responded.

"Then the obvious question now, Bill, is, 'Why do we harm ourselves with all this anger?'"

Mr. Dean couldn't miss the blank expression on my face now, so he continued. "Well obviously we don't intentionally harm ourselves, yet we know anger is physically and emotionally damaging, so we must be acting unconsciously." He paused, a smile appearing, allowing what he had just said to sink in.

I was glad he was taking this slowly.

He looked at me and raised his eyebrows as if to say, Are you following? May I continue? My mind was moving along at quite a clip. I had absorbed what he just said and nodded for more.

"Alright, then," he continued, pleased with my progress, "your mind is such a smart machine that it can create a kind of life of its own, all by itself, which it constantly strives to do." He knew this was a big pill to swallow and held up both hands making a pushing gesture, signaling for me to be patient and take all this very slowly.

He continued: "Whenever an event comes your way, your mind doesn't just accept it for what it is, it cleverly divides the event and presents it in a way that stimulates a reaction in you. Here's an example: You're driving along in your car and someone dangerously cuts in front of you. What do you do? You react. You get angry at that other driver and want to retaliate. You might even do something just as dangerous in return. Is that smart? Is risking your own life something a healthy, in-command person does to him- or herself? No! You can substitute a million examples for this one and they're all just as insane and destructive. But this is how our minds operate . . . ."

Mr. Dean sat back in his seat. I knew he wasn't finished, but I took this opportunity to ask a question. "But what else is there?" I became warm again as I asked this. It seemed like a stupid question, but at the same time I meant it. I was beginning to feel overwhelmed.

"The 'what else' is what your heart yearns for but has been running in circles to find. Running in circles because you've been listening to your mind to find it, and your mind isn't telling you anything new. Therefore, your mind cannot — it isn't capable of — leading you anywhere outside the circle.

'Conceive and believe' all you like, but that won't lead you to the happiness, success, and peace your heart yearns for."

He knew this was a huge bite for me, one that would take some time to assimilate. He smiled, watching the impact of what he just said materialize in my face. "Let me tell you a story, one you'll always remember, that illustrates all this:

"Once there was a rancher who was considered very wealthy by his friends and peers because he owned much land, many fine horses, and had a strong, healthy son to help him tend his ranch.

"One day all his horses escaped through a break in the fence and ran off. The rancher's friends and neighbors all gathered and said, 'This is so bad, this is very, very bad.'

"And the rancher replied, 'Why do you say this is bad?'

"A few days later, all the horses returned,

and with them came a strikingly handsome wild stallion, the likes of which had never been seen in those parts.

"The rancher's friends and neighbors returned and said, 'This is good, this is very, very good.'

"And the farmer replied, 'Why do you say this is good?'

"The rancher's son tried to tame the wild stallion, but it threw him and he broke his leg.

"The friends and neighbors gathered and said, 'This is bad, this is very bad.'

"And the rancher asked them again, 'Why do you say this is bad?'

"The country was going to war and government conscription officers showed up one day to take the son off to fight. But seeing that he was lame, they left him alone.

"Upon hearing this news, the neighbors and

friends came again and said, 'This is good, this is very, very good.'

"But the rancher simply scratched his head and said, 'Why do you say this is good?'

"So who in this little story represents your mind?" Mr. Dean asked me.

"The friends and neighbors," I said.

"And who is the hero?"

"The wise rancher."

"Right. So now let me really capture your attention and ask you this: Who in the story is more likely to live a successful life, including making and investing money wisely, and running a prosperous business?"

"The rancher . . . ." A smile came over me at the thought of this.

"Why?" Frank Dean asked, intently.

"Because," I answered slowly, "the friends and neighbors are running in a circle, and the rancher sees beyond it."

"Yes. Always keep this picture in mind when you catch yourself in another unexamined thought and another harmful emotion, Bill."

"Well are *all* emotions harmful?" I wondered aloud.

"I once had the pleasant opportunity of meeting privately with a movie star. She's still alive, so I won't reveal her name. She came from humble beginnings and rose to the grandest heights the world can offer anyone. She also has a very good understanding of what you and I are talking about here and demonstrated this during our meeting. She told me, 'Frank, never be fooled by those two impostors, success and failure.' Remember these words, Bill. And to answer your question: The mind thrives on emotions. That's how it traps you. Good and bad, success and failure, elation and depression — the opposites. Your whole life up to now has been a constant effort of avoiding something in order to gain its opposite. You're a slave, aren't you, believing in these two pictures your mind throws up in front of you as being the only possibilities?"

"Well then, what else is there?" I interjected, realizing that I had now asked this question twice.

With a broad smile, Mr. Dean reached the high point of our conversation. "That's what you can find out, Bill. There *is* something higher, there *is* a peace, there *is* an understanding, there *is* a wisdom above the never-ending circle that the world — and your mind — calls life!"

"So what do I do," I asked, sitting up in my seat, ready to receive the jolt I was sure was coming.

Mr. Dean paused again for what seemed to me to be several minutes.

"There's absolutely nothing to do. There's nothing you can do, except one thing." He paused again.

"The only thing you can do is to *see* what's really going on."

"That's all?! Well that's easy . . . ."

Mr. Dean laughed. It was a pleasant, understanding laugh though. I sat there looking puzzled. "Most of the time, Bill, you're lost in thought. Most of the time — and when I say this I mean 99.99 percent of the time — your thoughts are gripping you by the throat; there's no separation at all. You *are* those thoughts and, therefore, you *are* that anger, that depression, and even that excitement."

"You said 99.99 percent of the time. What's that hundredth of a percent when I'm not lost in thought?" I asked, feeling a bit defensive about what he just said.

"Was your breath ever taken away by a sunrise, a sunset, the ocean, or perhaps a symphony orchestra or a work of art, Bill? That was a genuine, natural gift. It was your higher response to receiving something from Nature, from Truth, if you will. You didn't create this sensation, you received it. All your common feelings and emotions are simply trumped up by your brain to create a false sense of life. Your brain can't create an awe-inspiring sunset; the best it can do is create anger and fear. Pitiful, isn't it . . . ."

"Well how do I avoid being 'lost in thought'?"

"Bill, do you know that your foot's tapping a mile a minute now, and that you're gripping the armrest here?"

I looked down and was embarrassed to see that he was right. I stopped my foot and loosened my grip. Why didn't I know I was doing these things?

"You were unaware of what you were doing because you were lost in thought, Bill," Mr. Dean continued, answering my silent question. "Being lost in thought means just that:

being oblivious to what's going on in your mind and what's going on around you. You've probably had this happen to you too, but at least you've heard someone tell how he or she drove a car for miles and miles and suddenly couldn't remember anything that happened the preceding half hour. That's not good, Bill! But that's how our minds operate, and it's a miracle that the world runs as well as it does."

"Wow . . . this is overwhelming, Mr. Dean. But surely more people than you say must know this. Why would I be one of only a handful of people to learn about this?"

"That's your brain talking now, raising questions that get in the way of your higher understanding. You can be sure it will put up a fight when you start questioning its operation and going against its directions. At times you'll feel like David battling Goliath."

"That sounds so ominous. It almost seems like it has a life of its own and is against my best interests . . . ."

"The life it has is *your* life, which you've willingly given over to it all these years. More than a handful of people are aware of this dual nature we all have, our brain versus a higher center that's a part of us. One of the reasons that *Dr. Jekyll and Mr. Hyde*, and stories like it, are perennial classics is because they reveal this dual nature that we all *know* but seldom acknowledge. But very, very few people have the courage to follow through and do the work of mastering this brain we carry around."

"Work? What work, exactly?"

"It takes much energy to stay awake and aware enough to even get glimpses into all this taking place within ourselves. That is, it takes energy to stay in what I'll call the Here-and-Now. If you don't know that your foot's tapping, that your hand is clamped onto an armrest, or where you've just driven your car for the past twenty miles, you're asleep mentally — lost in thought. If you're lost in thought, you're being pulled this way and that by every emotion that passes through your mind, and those emotions are painful — every one of them. The way to stay mentally awake is to know where you are at the moment, to feel your feet on the floor, to feel the temperature of the air against your face, and to see what's going through your mind at the moment. Think of your mind as a rushing torrent — a river that never stops. If you're watching this river rushing past, then you're not *in* the river. But if you are not watching the swift current, you're trapped in it. Do you see now?"

"Yes, I think so."

"That's where you start, Bill. You just watch and watch and watch. When you meet someone, notice how afraid you are of that person. And then ask yourself why you feel afraid and you'll find that it's because you want something from that person. What do you want?

You want him or her to like you and approve of you!

"You were exhibiting this sort of fear in your conversation with our stewardess."

That statement hit me with a jolt — of truth!

"As you have these realizations, you'll be shocked. And the more times you're shocked, the better. In this way, you can jolt yourself awake!

"Make it your new aim to know what's going on in and around you. At first you may remember this only two or three times a day, but the more you work at it, the more frequent will be your moments of clarity. It's work, Bill. It's tiring, and you'll find that your mind will put up quite a fight. But the more you do it, the more you'll see that this is the only aim worth having. You'll one day realize that waking up is what this life is all about, for only wakefulness provides what your heart truly longs for."

"Boy! What a flight this turned out to be! I almost feel like I have a new burden, now that you've told me all this."

"That's your mind's reaction again, Bill. Is having wisdom, knowing the right thing to do every moment, and living without fear, anger, depression, and disappointment a burden? See how ridiculous that seems? Yet that's your mind talking, and that's what's been in control of your life. It's what's in charge of virtually everyone's life even though I believe everyone does get his or her chance to follow this path. But that's just an inkling I've had. It's a difficult path to follow, but you have to *stay on it*. As the Bible tells us, once you take up the plow, there can be no looking back . . . ."

"So if someone — most people — doesn't somehow make it to this road . . . ," I was thinking out loud,

" . . . He exists on a level way below his potential, and he exists at the mercy of the Law of Accident." Mr. Dean had finished my sentence with another earthshaking conslusion of his own. He knew this would stimulate a reaction from me, and he waited.

"The Law of Accident?" is all I had to say to let him know I was ready to learn more.

"If people are sleepwalking, unaware of what's really going on within and without, out of control with worry about their future, what are they?"

"Well, um, robots?"

"Yes — machines! And if you place a bunch of machines in a room and set them loose, what do you have?"

"Ah, chaos?"

"Yes! And how else would you describe your life — isn't it chaotic?"

"Well, yes, I guess it is . . . ."

"Absolutely it is, Bill. Don't you run this way and that, scurrying to do whatever you *think* you have to to keep everything under control? And all the time you know that at any moment it all could fall apart. What's the first thought on your mind when you get out of bed in the morning? Isn't it, 'I wonder what life's going to throw at me today'? That's fear, Bill, and that's how everyone lives — in constant fear."

This hit me hard. I sensed all kinds of emotions going on within me. What I noticed most was anger. But why should I be angry? I once heard that anger is a result of not knowing what to do. So if I knew — really knew — that what Mr. Dean was saying wasn't true, why would I be angry? No, I sensed that what Mr. Dean was saying was absolutely right and that an incredible secret, a monumental truth, had been revealed to me this evening. Nevertheless, I felt weak.

"So we have this roomful of machines scurrying about. And each one is bumping into a wall here and another machine there, all the time worried — fearful — that he won't end up where he wants, or that he's not going in the right direction. And on those chance occasions when he does end up someplace in the room where he always desired to be, he's frantic with the fear that he'll get knocked out of that spot sooner or later . . . . Does this sound like anything you're familiar with, Bill?" he smiled.

"Yes, sir. It sounds like the world." I paused to think a bit. "But what about those people who make it, like big businessmen, or movie stars?" I was hoping I had thought of a loophole.

"Don't you watch TV or read the newspaper? Those people are the ones at the bottom of just about every piece of bad news you see or read. And can you figure out why?"

"They think they have more to lose, so they're more frantic?" I answered.

"Yes. There's absolutely nothing wrong with money or position or fame, but what's the use if those are also the sources of your greatest fears? Ralph Waldo Emerson once said, if a man owns a piece of land, the piece of land owns him. He knew what material success can do to people. Wouldn't you rather be an awake, alert human being who — when he attains all those goodies — truly enjoys them, and doesn't let *them* own *him*?"

"Yes, of course. The world of common thoughts and common behaviors actually sounds terrifying when you look at it this way," I reasoned.

"And 'terrifying' isn't too strong a word to describe this either. Under the Law of Accident, finding yourself suddenly up on a pedestal that you know could be knocked out from under you at any moment is not what you'd call a peaceful life — it's a nightmare actually." But if you realize that your success is accidental, and quit investing your whole self in it, you can avoid this nightmare." We were beginning to descend into Los Angeles and Mr. Dean turned to look out the window.

I watched him and thought of all my Dad had told me about this man over the years — this very man I was sitting next to in First Class! If only my Dad could be here now . . . . I knew Mr. Dean had done and had it all. Even though the average person wouldn't know him, in the business world he was revered. His face was on the covers of industry magazines. And here he was, sharing this time with me — a total stranger really — instead of doing all the important things I'm sure he would otherwise be doing.

"Mr. Dean, are you traveling to Los Angeles to give a speech?"

He turned from the small window and chuckled. "No, I don't give very many speeches any longer, Bill. I gave hundreds and hundreds of the kind your Dad heard me deliver in New York, but the more I learned of what I'm telling you tonight, and the more I progressed along these lines of self-study, the more I realized that what I had been saying at those gatherings wasn't helping anyone at all."

"Well you sure made a positive impact on my Dad. I don't think he admired anyone as much as he did you," I added.

"There were some right ideas in those speeches, but I didn't know then what I know now. Those talks were what they call 'motivational,' which is nothing more than simply trumping up feelings, like a coach does with his football team. It may get a single job done, but it's short-lived — it's not real. You can only blow a balloon up so many times before it gets weak and breaks.

"These ideas I'm telling you of, Bill, are all-important, but they're not all-popular. As I began to bring them into my talks more and more, I saw that I wasn't getting repeat bookings from groups and organizations that used to bring me back year after year.

"But an enlightened man I had the privilege and gift of knowing taught me to always do the right thing, no matter what the consequences, and the consequences would always be right. He also said, 'The truer, the fewer.' That man was named Vernon Howard and he wrote several incisive books on this subject of waking up to our true potential and learning to transcend this limiting brain of ours. He definitely broke through to another world, the one we're speaking of. Remember his name when you want to take the next step away from what's holding you back, Bill."

"So you're out on the West Coast just for business then?" I persisted even though I felt like I was being pushy.

"You know, I don't know why I've come to Los Angeles. The past few days I've had the strongest urge to get on a plane and come out here. So, I did! Here I am, and I have a hunch that it may have been just so you and I

could have this little chat . . . ." He smiled
and raised his eyebrows.

"It's too bad our time together was so
short," I thought aloud.

"Why do you say it's bad?" he asked animat-
edly.

We both smiled and prepared for landing.

I thought of how fortuitous it was that I
was sitting in the only empty row of seats in
the back of the plane and was requested to
come forward to First Class. I also wondered
whether, if the situation were reversed, and I
were asked to leave First Class and go sit in
coach, I would have been so quick to oblige.
My brain would have told me that coach is a
"worse" place, and I might have resisted the
invitation. And what if Frank Dean had been
sitting *there*?

Perhaps he's right, and each of us does get
at least one opportunity to escape . . . .